Tárrega for Guitar

40 leichte Originalwerke und Bearbeitungen
40 Easy Original Works and Arrangements

Herausgegeben von
Edited by
Martin Hegel

ED 21857
ISMN 979-0-001-19797-7

www.schott-music.com

Mainz · London · Berlin · Madrid · New York · Paris · Prague · Tokyo · Toronto

Vorwort

Francisco Tárrega (1852–1909) ist als Gitarrist und vor allem als Komponist eine der wichtigsten Persönlichkeiten in der Geschichte der Gitarre. Seine immense Bedeutung in Bezug auf die Entwicklung der Gitarre innerhalb der letzten 200 Jahre kann gar nicht hoch genug eingeschätzt werden. Schon zu seiner Zeit war er nicht nur einer der führenden Gitarristen, sondern auch ein begnadeter Didaktiker und vor allem Komponist. Bis heute zählen seine Stücke zu den meistgespielten des Gitarrenrepertoires.

Nach den enormen Fortschritten im frühen 19. Jahrhundert, der Blütezeit der Gitarre, hat Tarrega die Gitarrentechnik nochmals auf seine Weise revolutioniert, indem er die Satztechnik von Fernando Sor und Mauro Giuliani genauestens analysiert und auf seine Art weitergeführt hat. Tárrega schaffte es wie kein Zweiter, einen spätromantischen Satz mit wenigen präzise ausgewählten Tönen auf die Gitarre zu übertragen, um somit in diesen kleinen salonartigen Meisterwerken die künstlerischen und klanglichen Ausdrucksmöglichkeiten der Gitarre zu erweitern. Nicht nur die verschiedenen Aspekte der Gitarrentechnik, sondern auch viele andere Standards wie Körperhaltung, Fingerstellung, Gitarrengröße und -form gehen auf ihn zurück und haben bis heute Geltung.

Die vorliegende Sammlung bietet einen Einstieg in Tárregas Œuvre und beinhaltet die leichtesten seiner Kompositionen, von kleinen Etüden und Präludien bis hin zu kleineren Vortrags- und Konzertstücken. Ergänzend wurden vereinfachte Arrangements und Auszüge seiner bekanntesten Werke sowie eine Auswahl aus seinen unzähligen didaktischen Übungsstücken hinzugefügt.

Auch wenn der Musik Tárregas üblicherweise ein charakteristischer Fingersatz zugrunde liegt, der die Stücke gewissermaßen veredelt, wurde der Fingersatz bei den vorliegenden leichten bis mittelschweren Stücken insgesamt vereinfacht, um überbordendes Lagen-, Barréespiel und Glisssandi eher zu vermeiden. Aus diesem Grund sind auch die verschiedenen Verzierungen und Bindungen optional angegeben. Dem fortgeschrittenen Spieler sind in dieser Hinsicht mit einem elaborierteren Fingersatz selbstverständlich keine Grenzen gesetzt.

Martin Hegel

Preface

Francisco Tárrega (1852–1909) is one of the most important figures in the history of the guitar – as a guitarist and above all as a composer. His immense significance in relation to the development of the guitar in the last two centuries cannot be valued highly enough. In his time he was not only one of the leading guitarists, but a gifted teacher and composer, too: his pieces number among the most often played in the guitar repertoire to this day.

After great advances in the early 19th Century, the heyday of the guitar, Tárrega brought about another revolution in guitar technique through his analysis and further development of the work of Fernando Sor and Mauro Giuliani. Tárrega was uniquely successful in adapting late Romantic music for the guitar with a few carefully chosen notes, extending the artistic and expressive range of guitar sounds in these little masterpieces of the salon. Not only various aspects of guitar technique can be traced back to him, but essential matters such as physical stance, finger positions, size and shape of guitar, too, that are still in use today.

The present collection offers an introduction to Tárrega's work that includes the easiest of his compositions, starting with little studies and preludes and moving on to modest pieces for concert performance. Simplified arrangements and extracts from his best-known works have also been included, along with a selection of his innumerable didactic exercises.

While Tárrega's music generally uses a characteristic fingering pattern that enhances the pieces in some respects, here fingering has been simplified throughout for pieces of easy to intermediate difficulty, so as to avoid excessive reliance on higher positions, barrée and glissandi. For the same reason, the various ornaments and slurs are shown as optional. For advanced players of course there are no limits on using more elaborate fingerings.

Martin Hegel
Translation Julia Rushworth

Inhalt / Contents

7 kleine Etüden / 7 Little Studies

I. Estudio en do

Francisco Tárrega
1852–1909

II. Estudio en mi menor

IV. Estudio en la

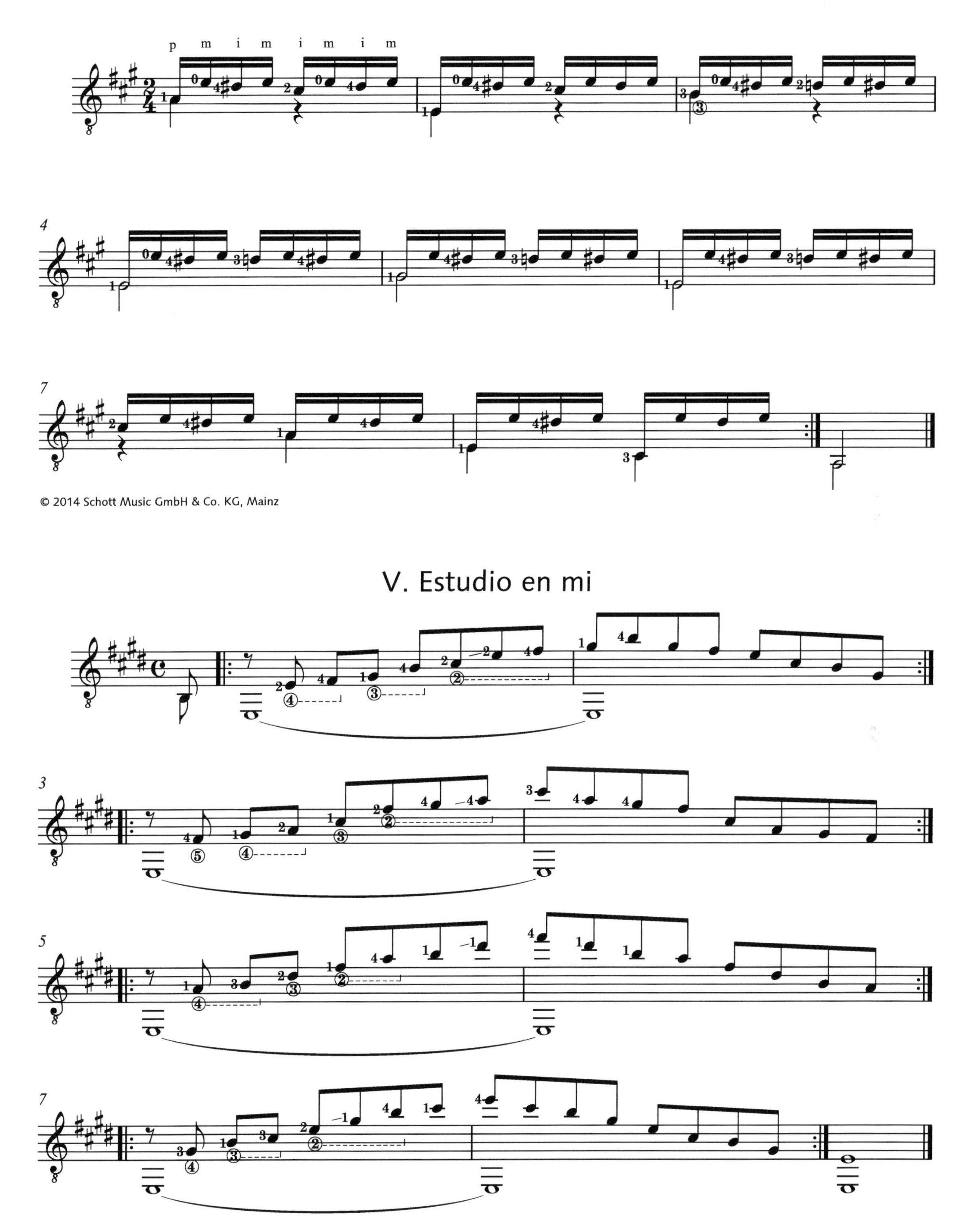

V. Estudio en mi

VI. Estudio en re

VII. Estudio en la

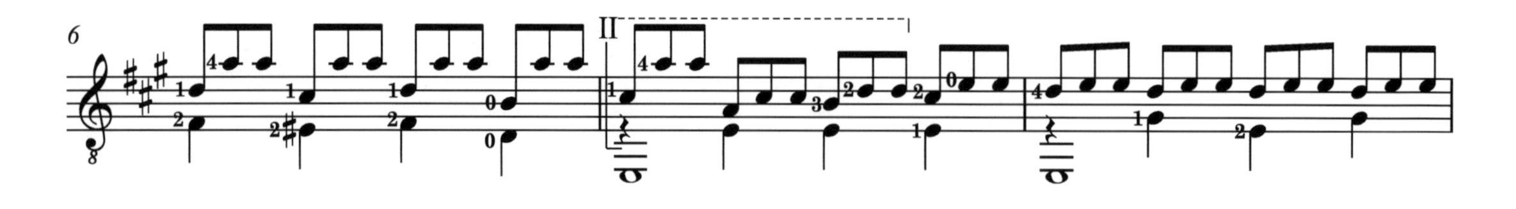

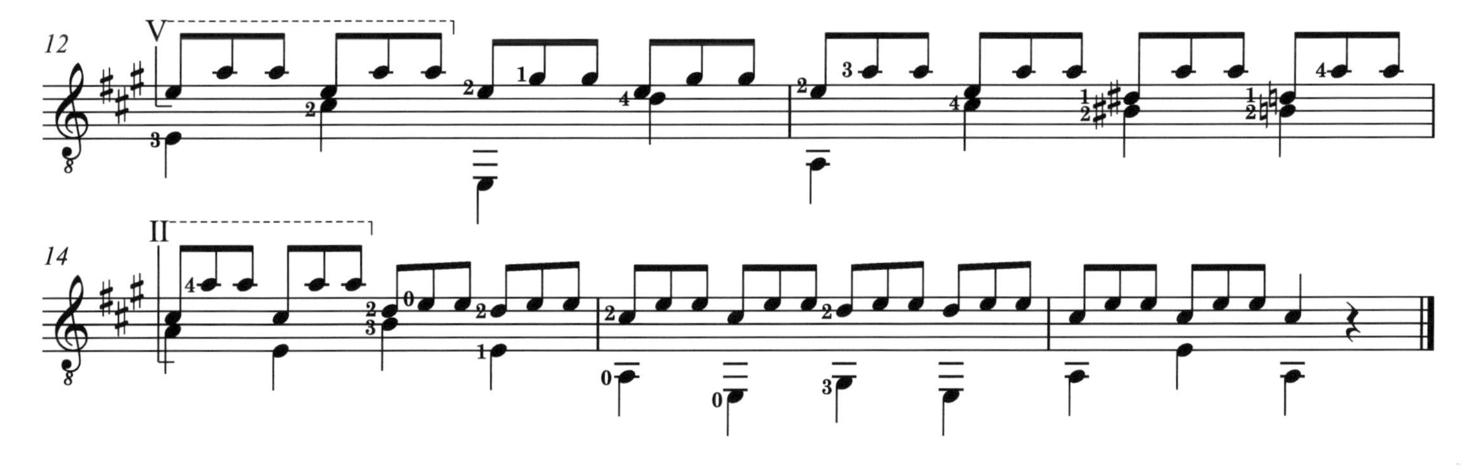

12 kleine Präludien / 12 Little Preludes

I. Preludio en la

Francisco Tárrega

II. Preludio en la

III. Preludio en la

VI. Preludio en la

VII. Preludio en sol

VIII. Preludio en la menor

Andantino

IX. Preludio en la menor

Allegro moderato

X. Preludio en re

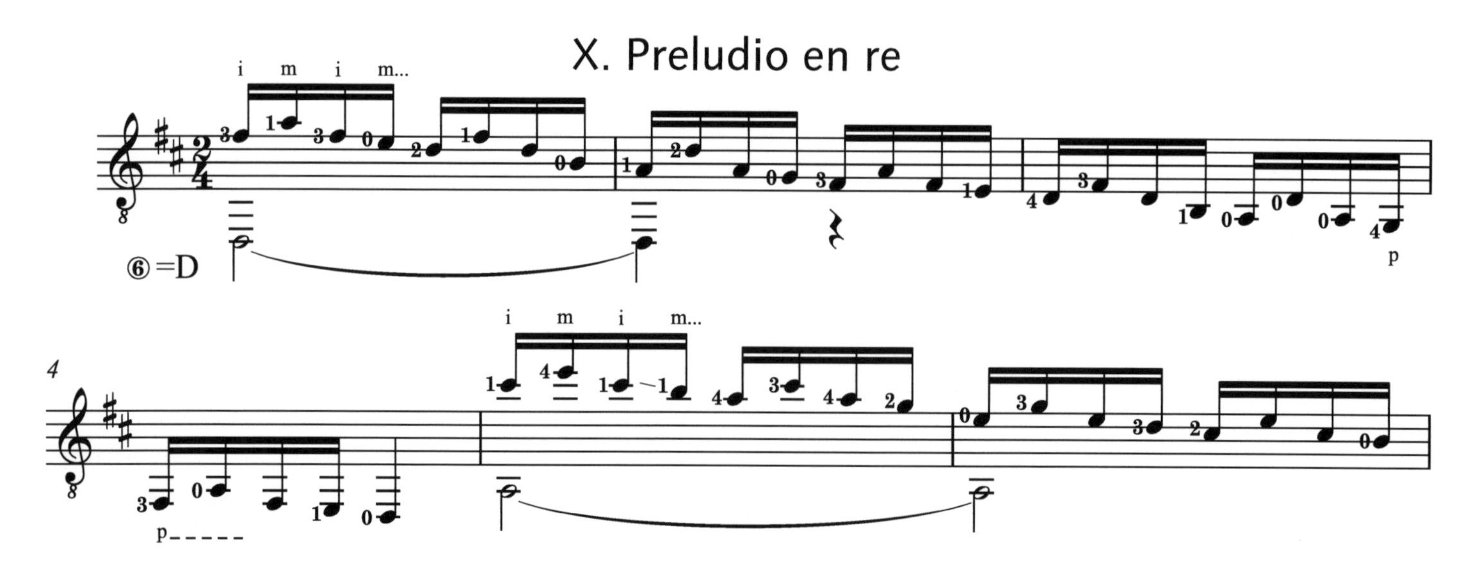

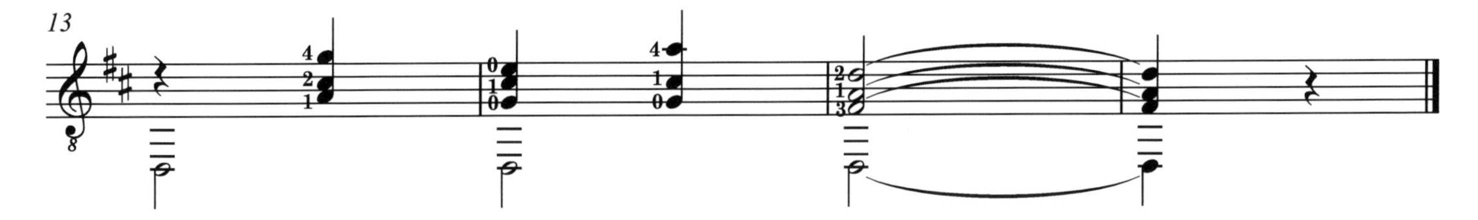

XI. Preludio en re

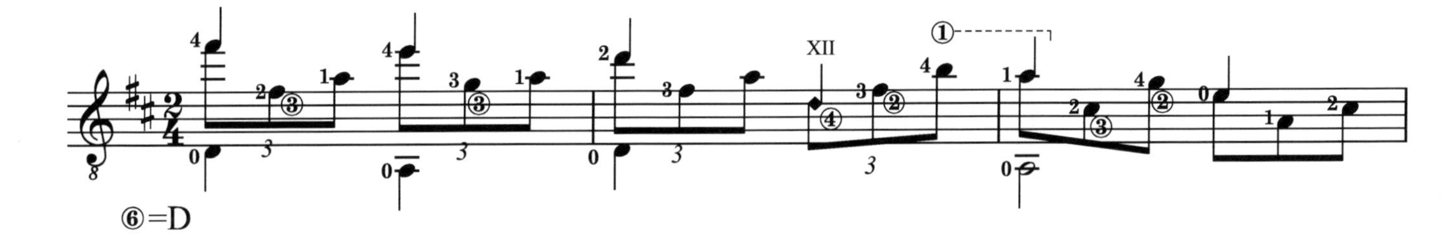

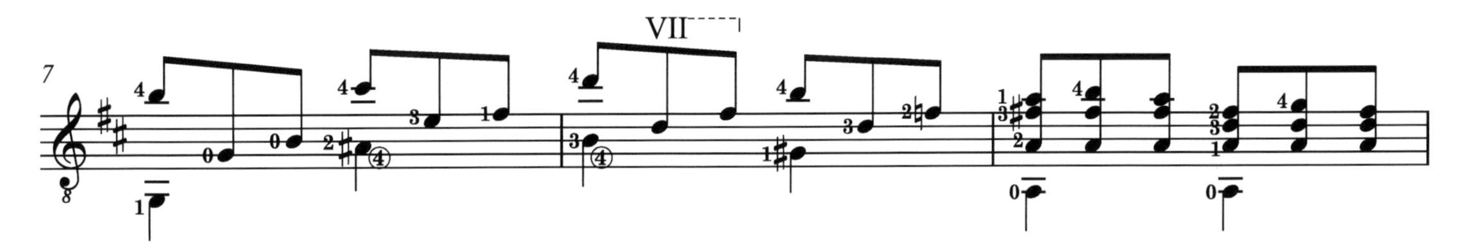

XII. Preludio en re

Adelita

Mazurka

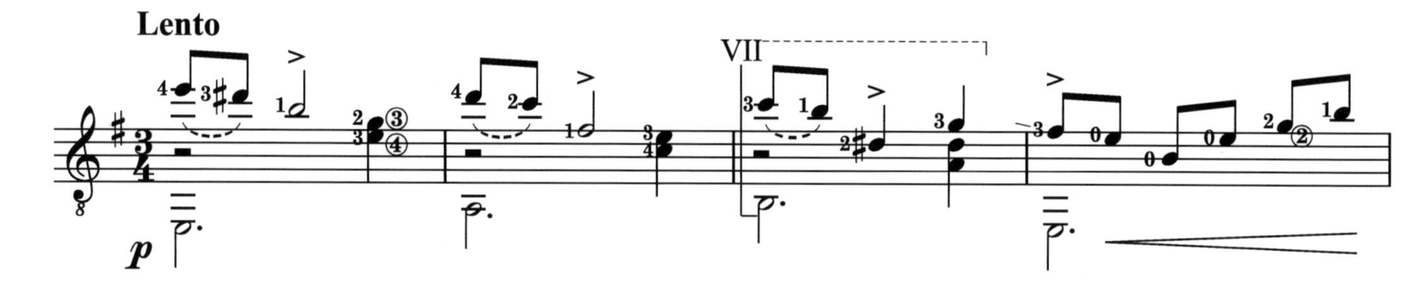

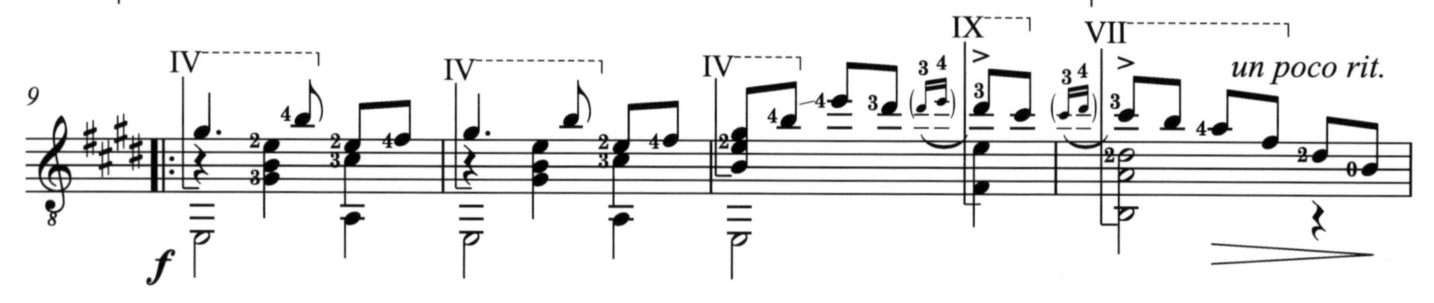

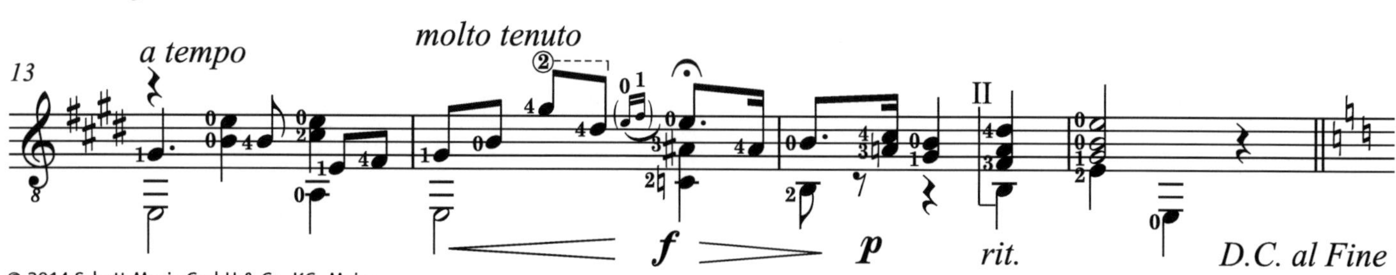

Mazurka

Lágrima

Andante

Preludio

Pavana

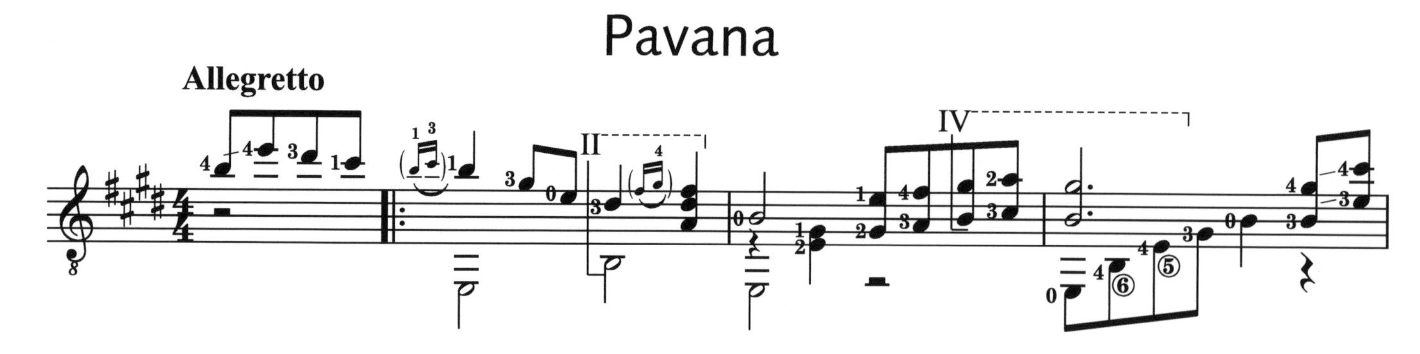

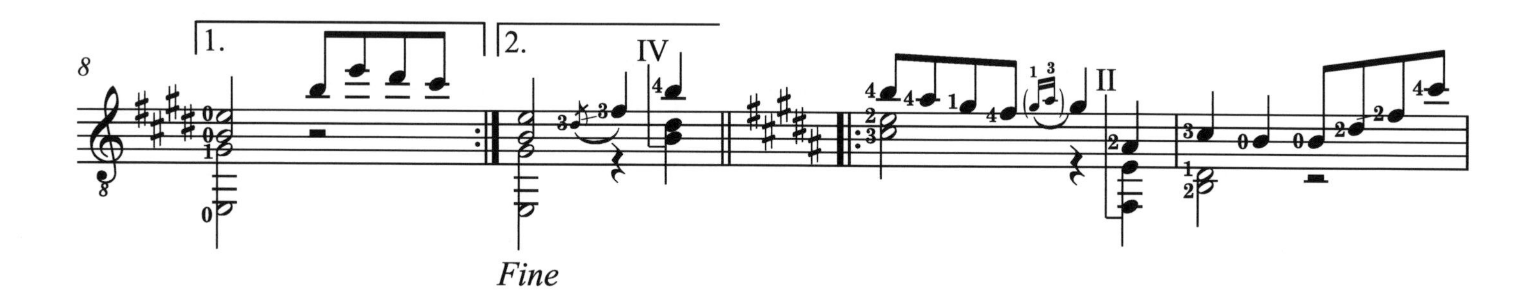

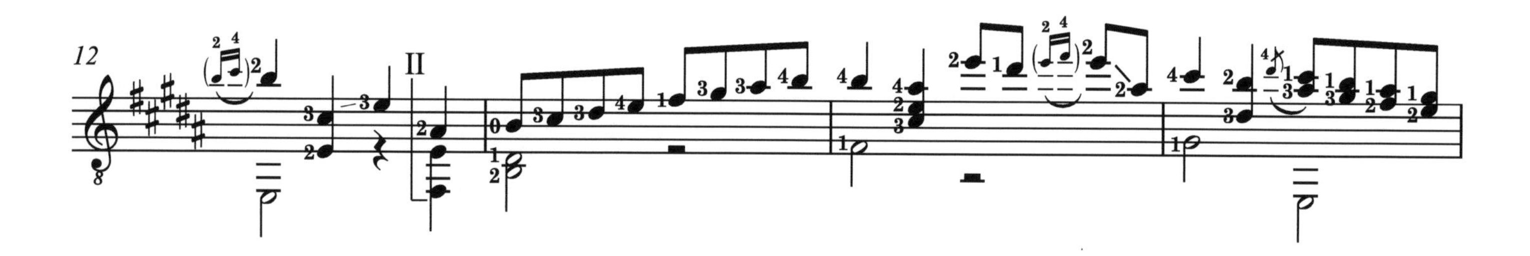

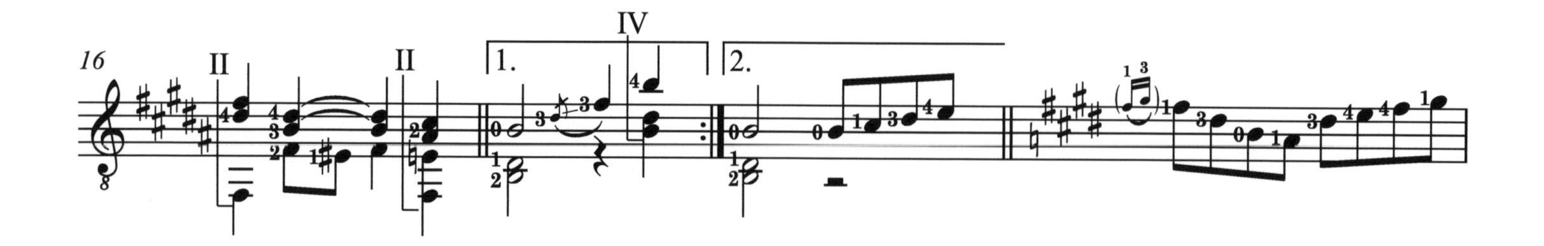

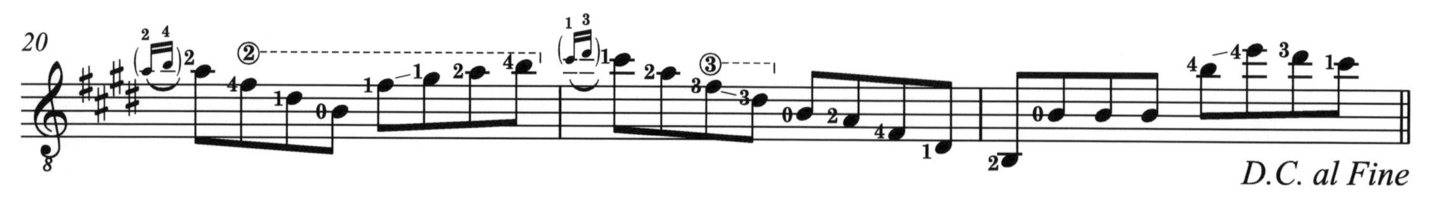

5 leichte Bearbeitungen / 5 Easy Arrangements

I. Recuerdos de la Alhambra

Francisco Tárrega
Arr.: Martin Hegel

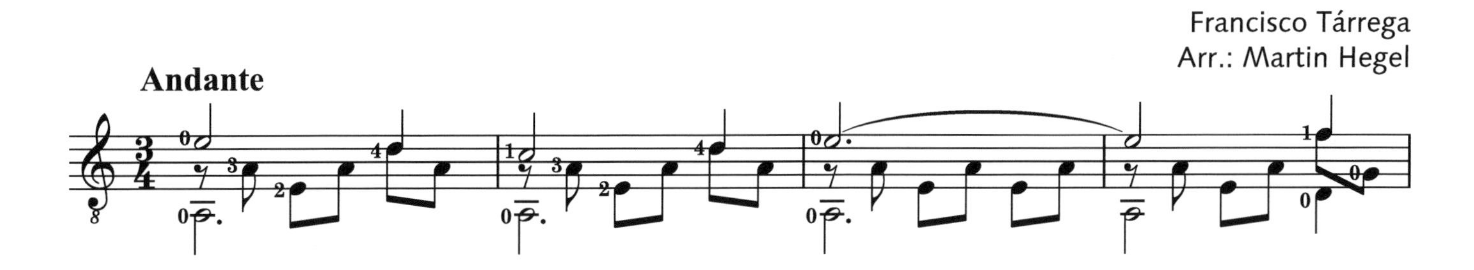

II. Adelita

Francisco Tárrega
Arr.: Martin Hegel

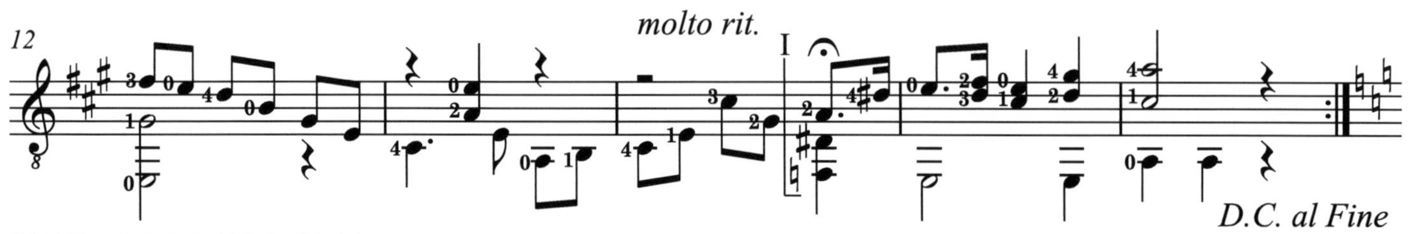

III. Lágrima

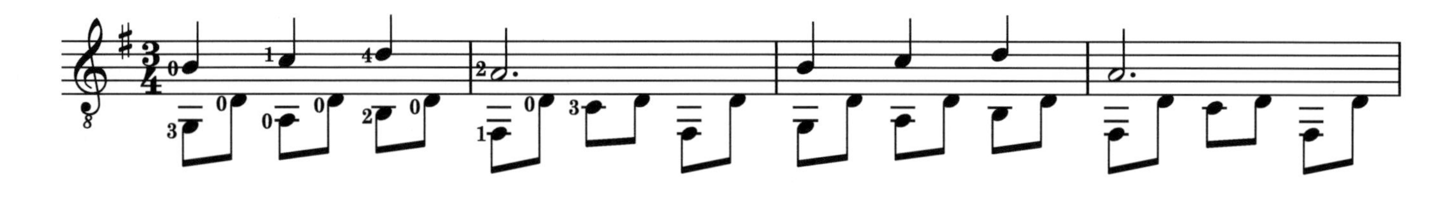

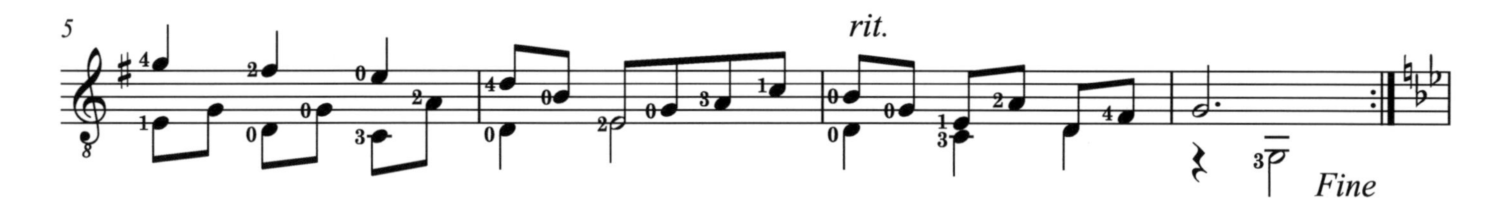

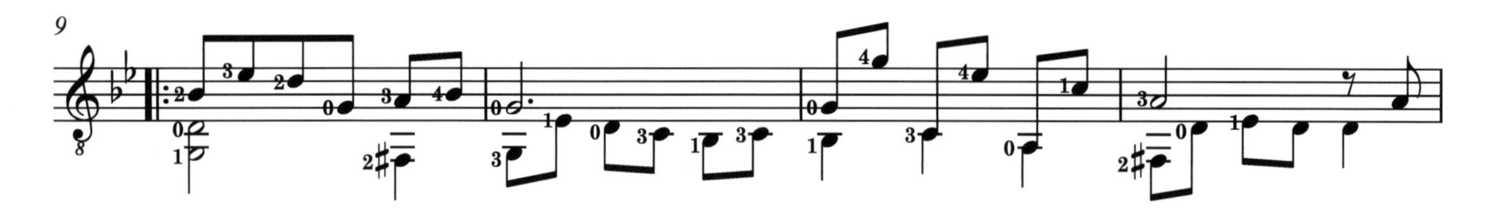

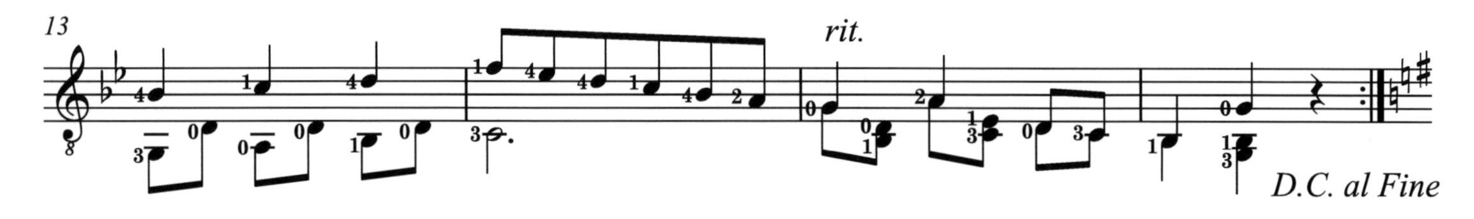

IV. Capricho arabe

Francisco Tárrega
Arr.: Martin Hegel

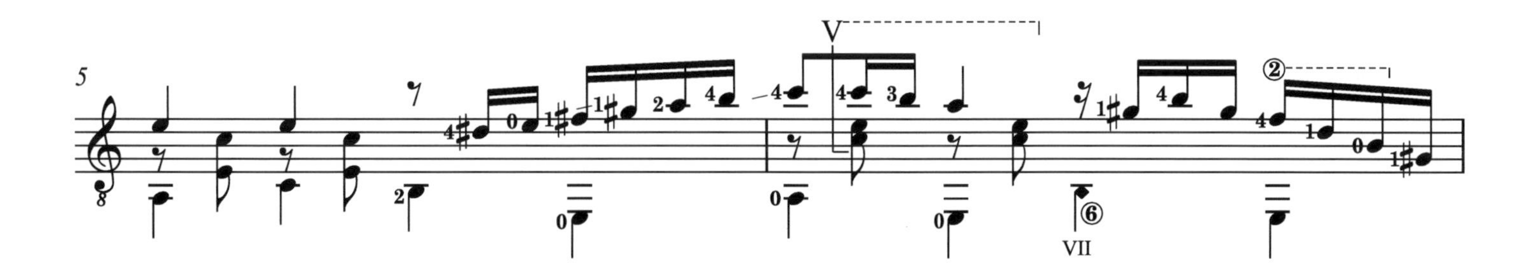

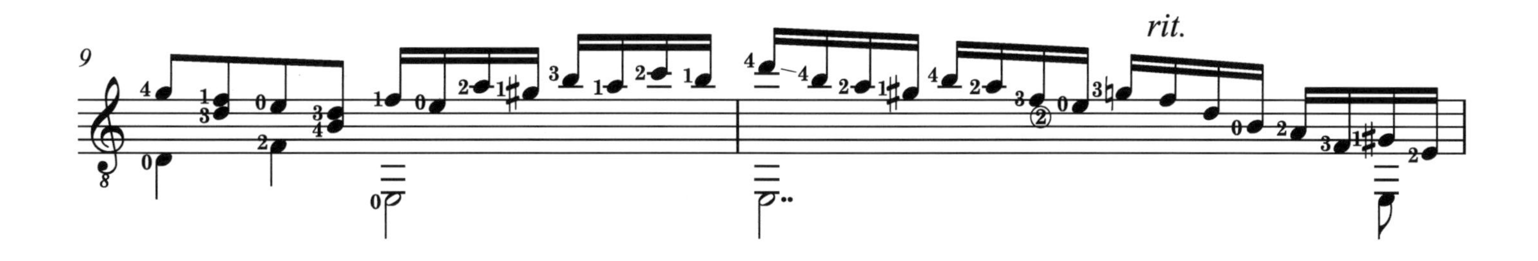

V. Gran Vals

Francisco Tárrega
Arr.: Martin Hegel

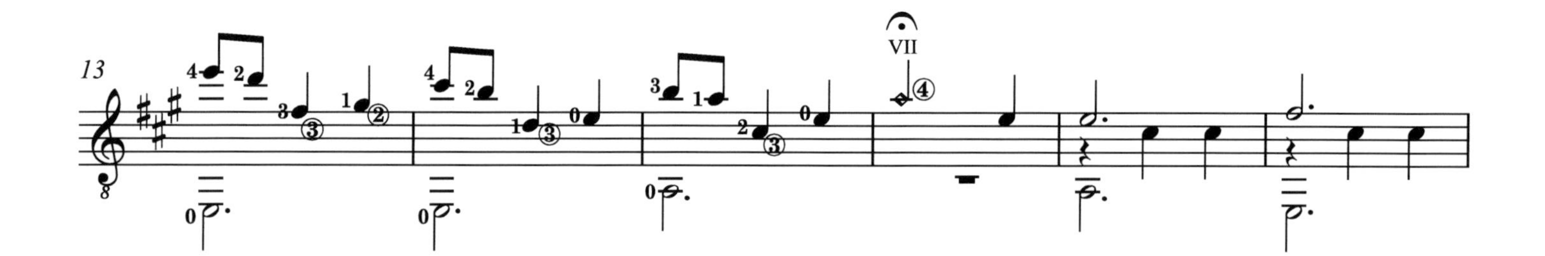

Endecha

Preludio

Francisco Tárrega

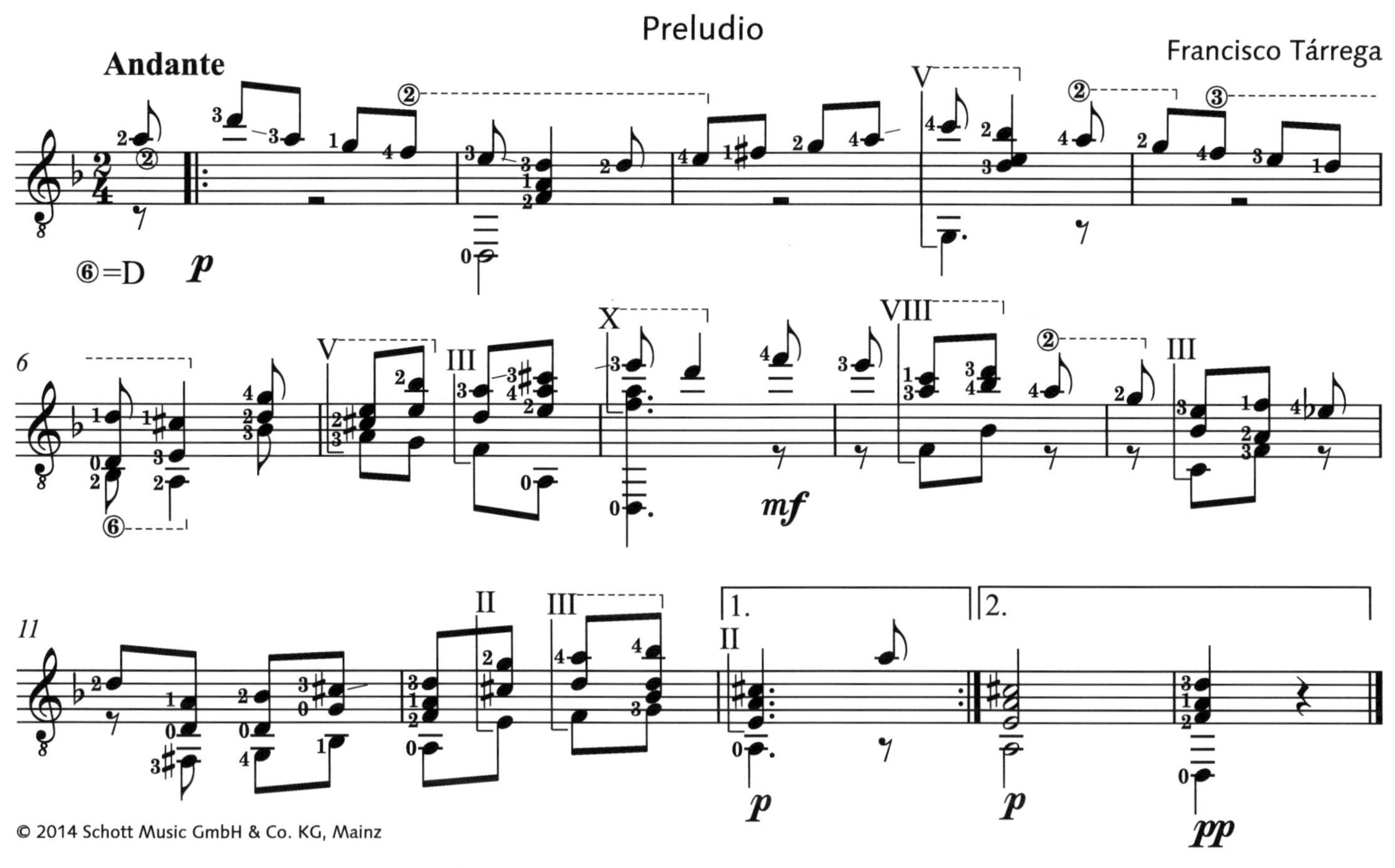

Oremus

Preludio

Francisco Tárrega

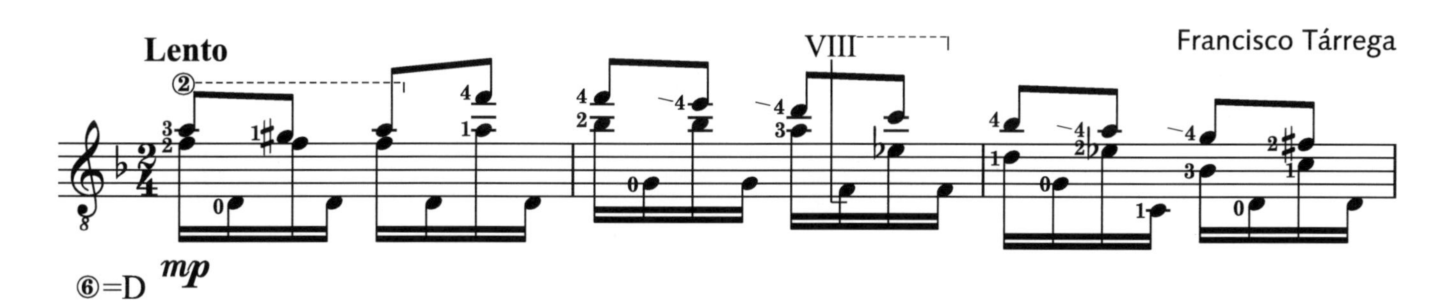

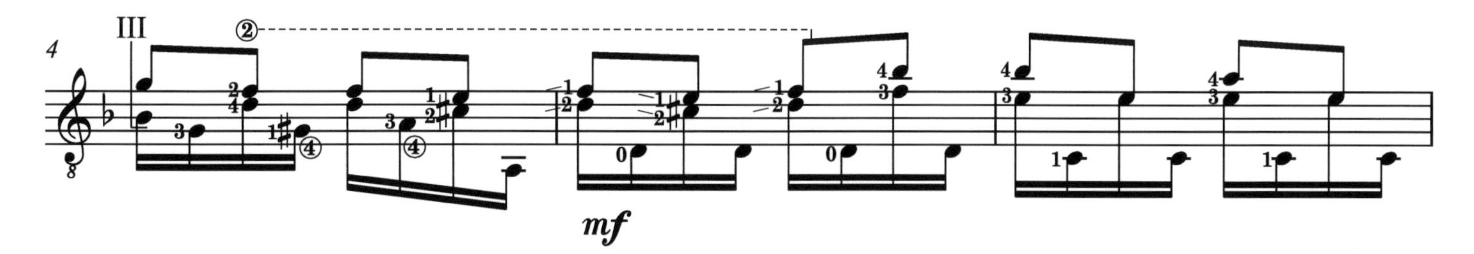

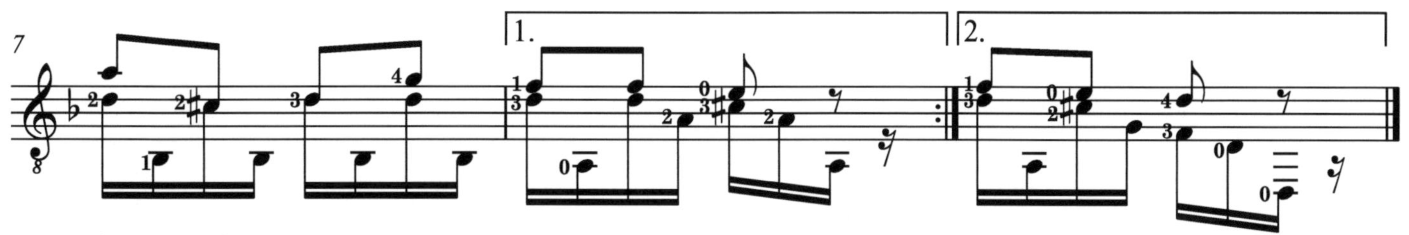

Sueño

Mazurka

Francisco Tárrega

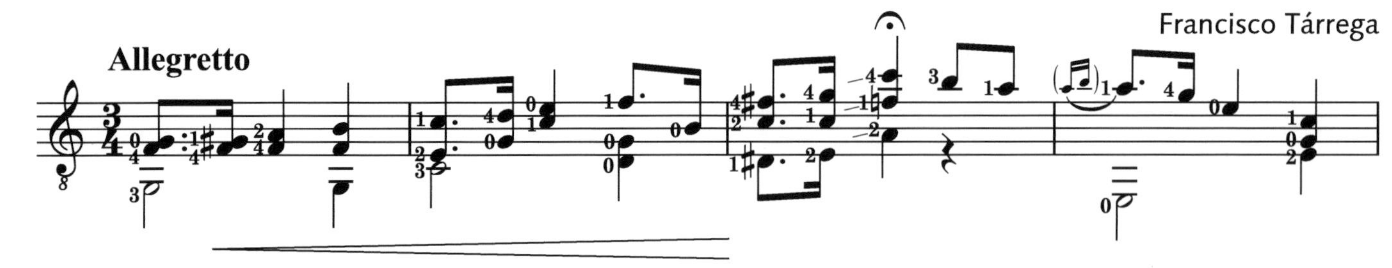

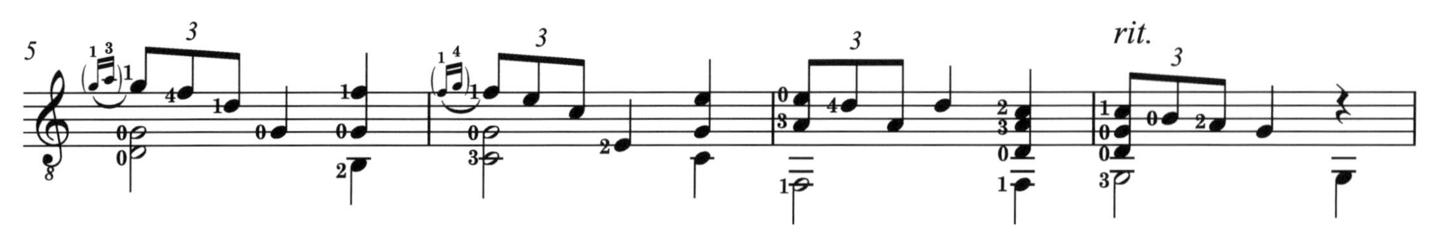

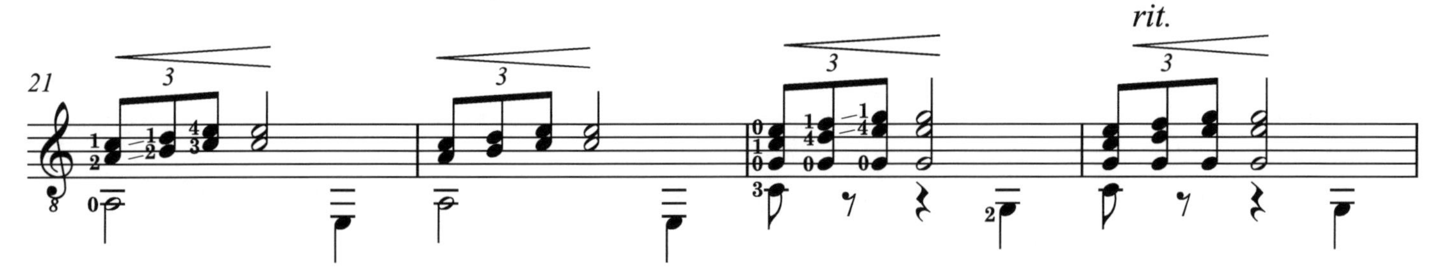

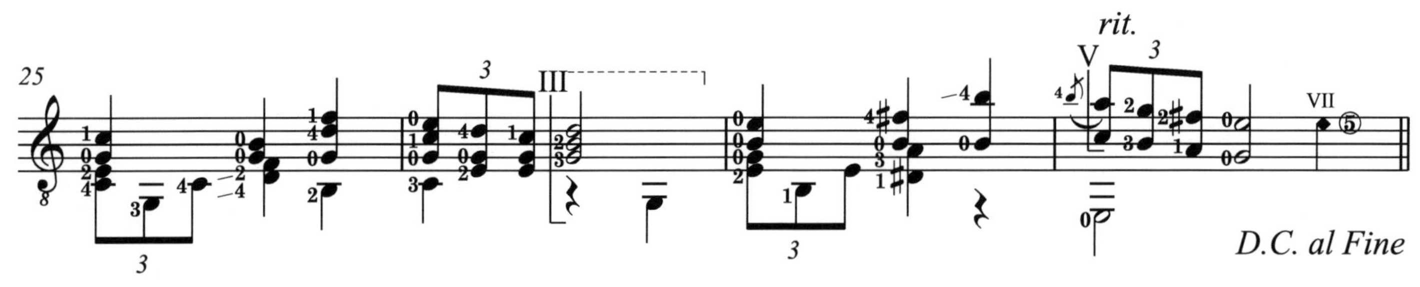

Isabel

Vals

Francisco Tárrega

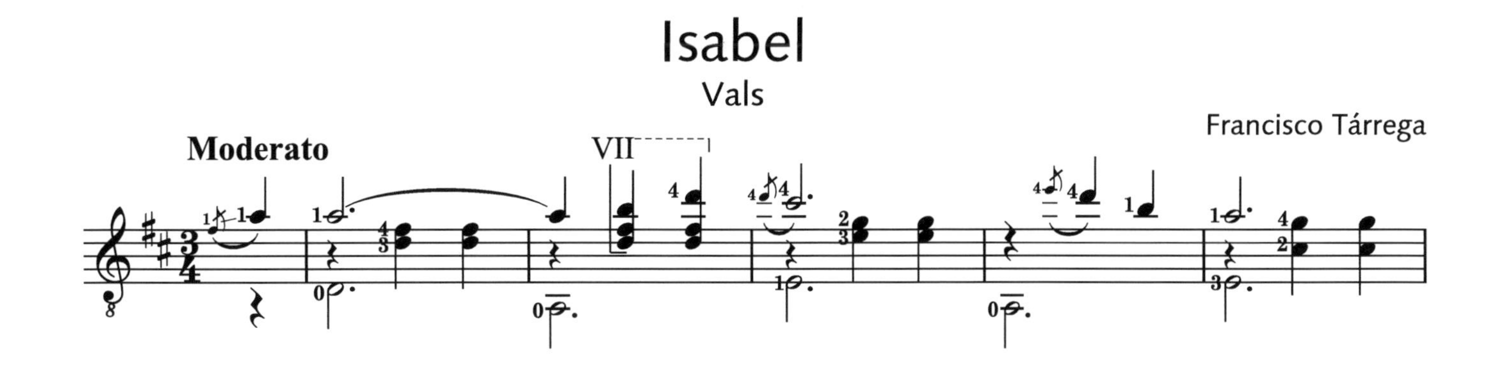

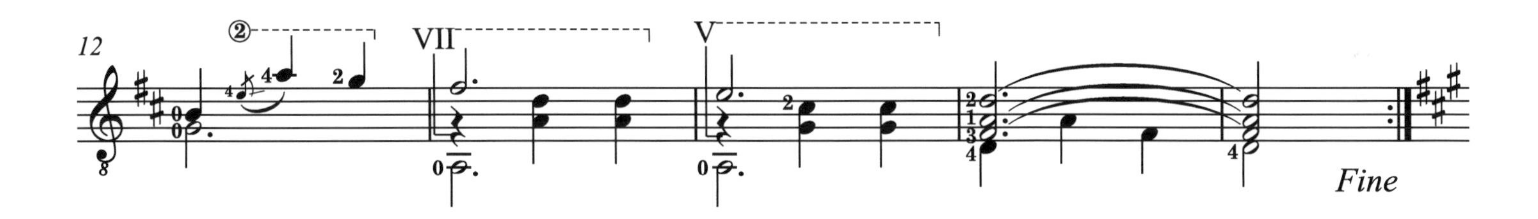

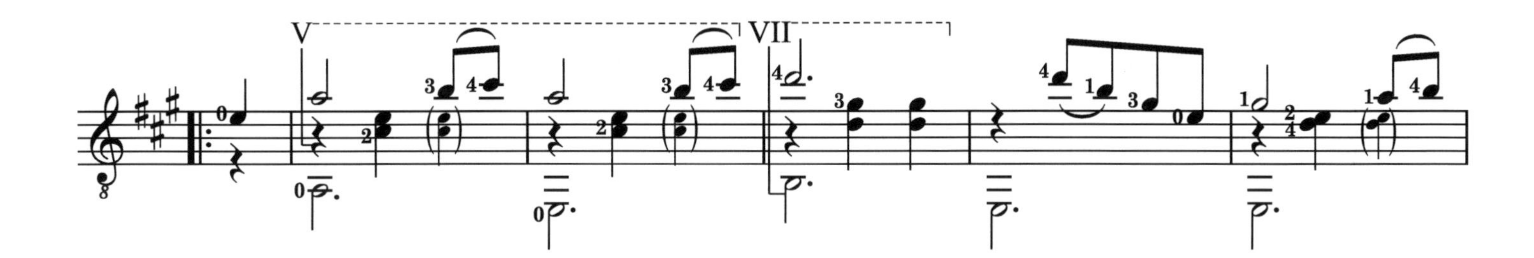

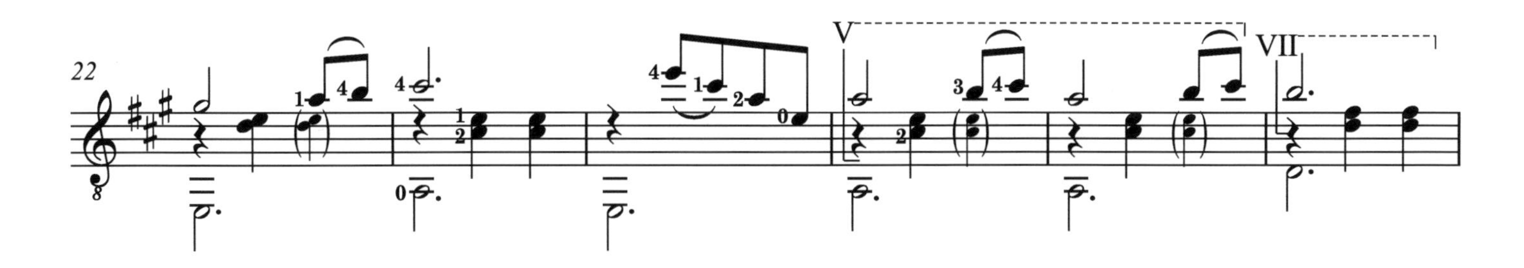

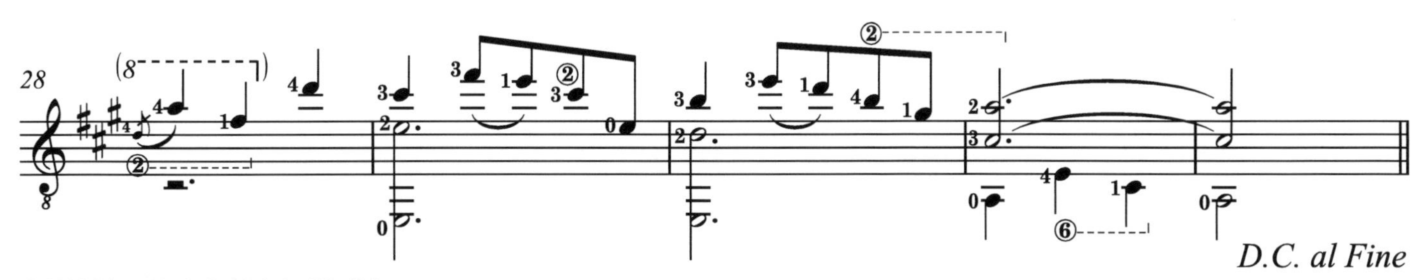

Tango

Francisco Tárrega

Vals en re

Francisco Tárrega

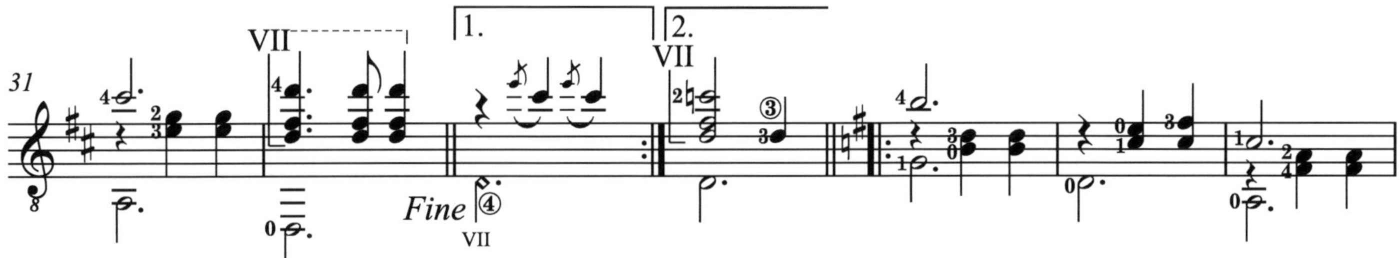

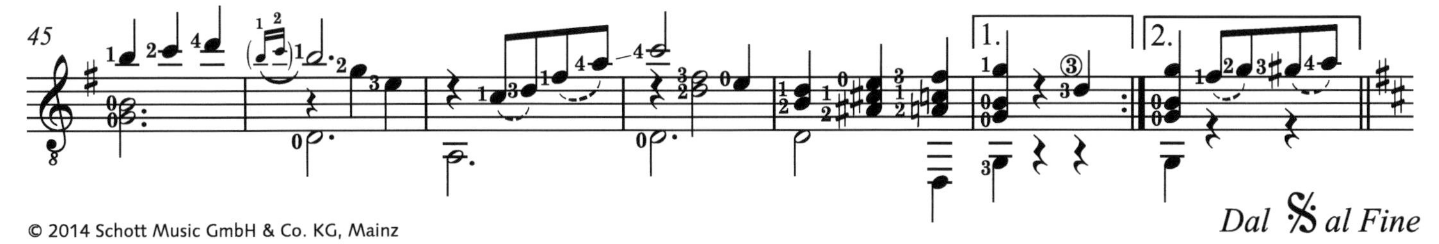

Pepita

Polka

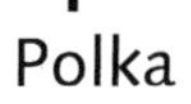

Francisco Tárrega

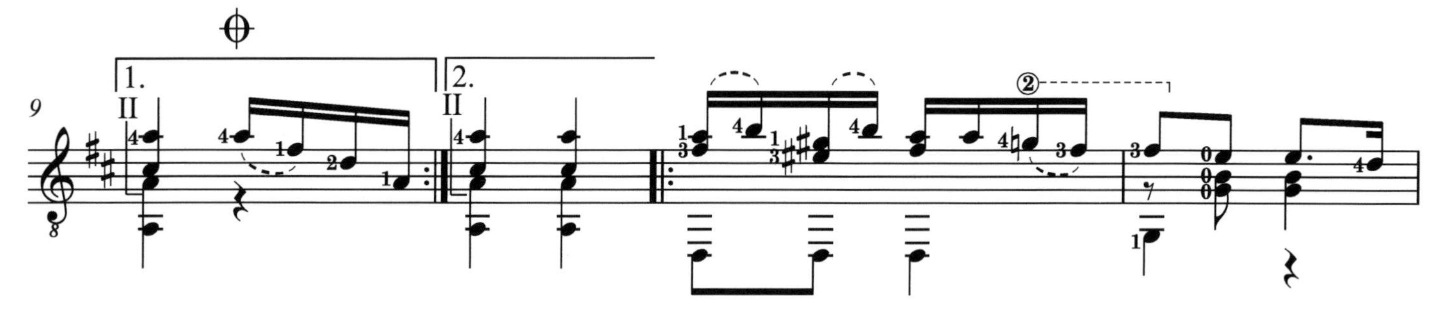

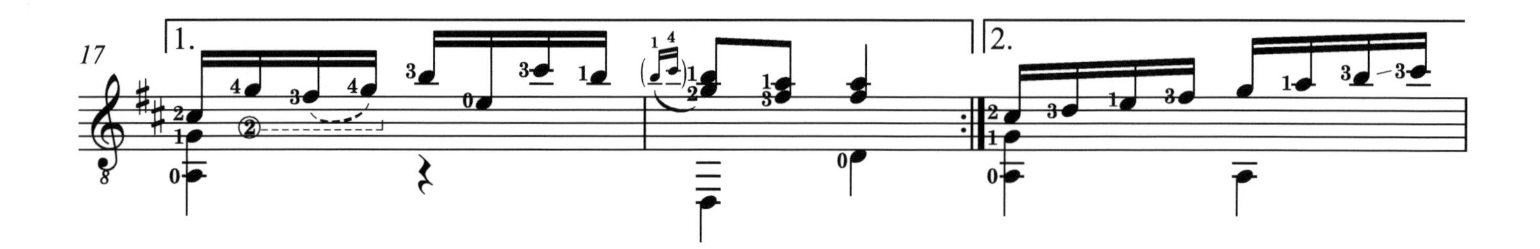

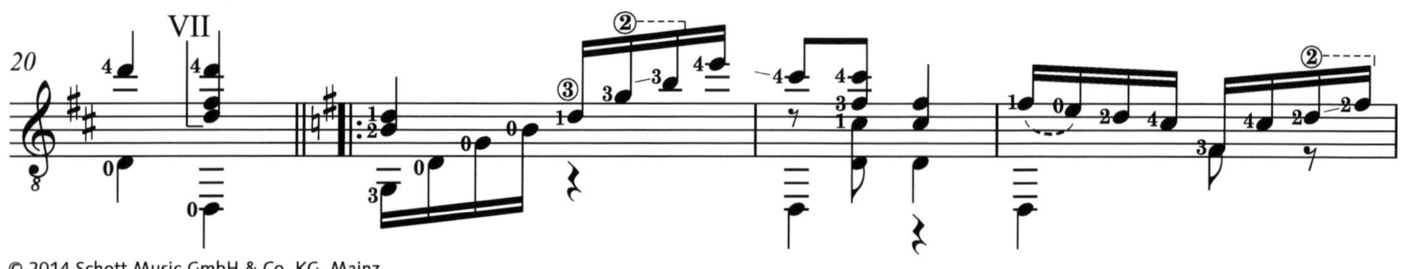

V

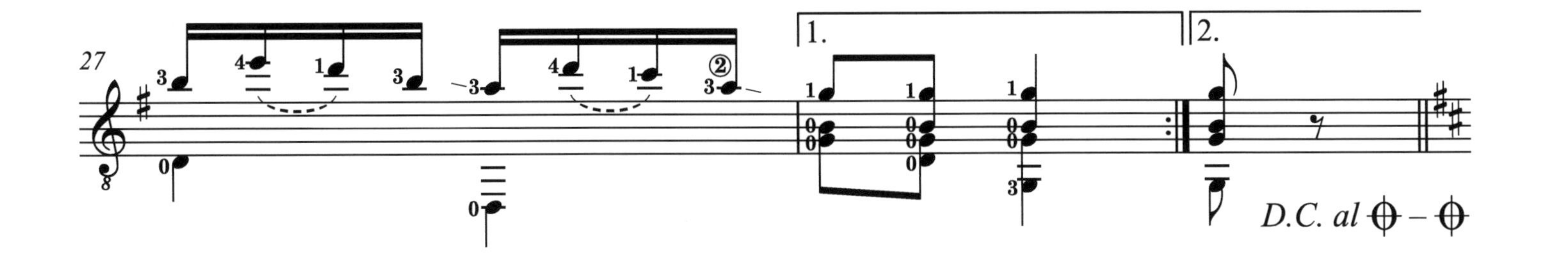
1.
2.
D.C. al

Coda

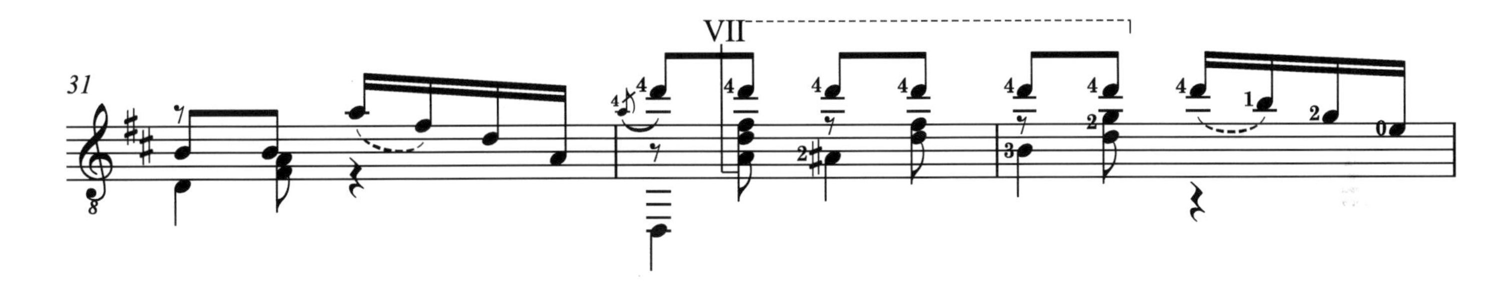
VII

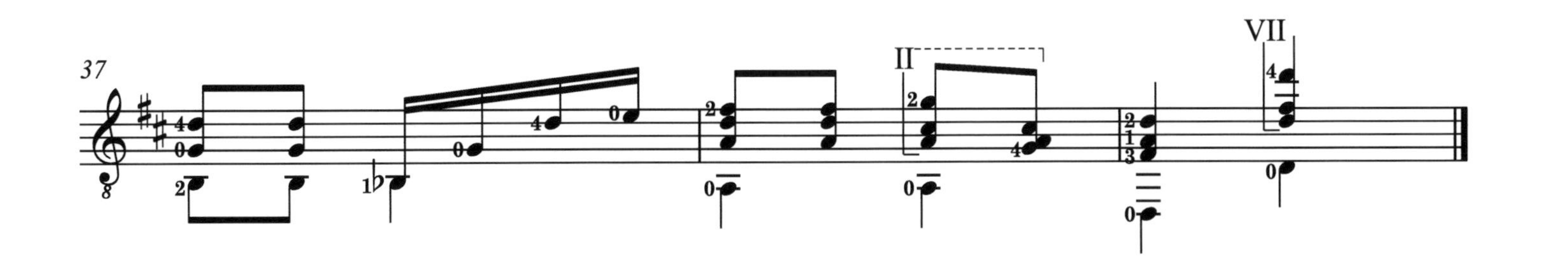
II
VII

Maria

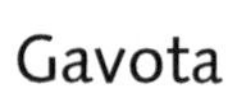

Francisco Tárrega

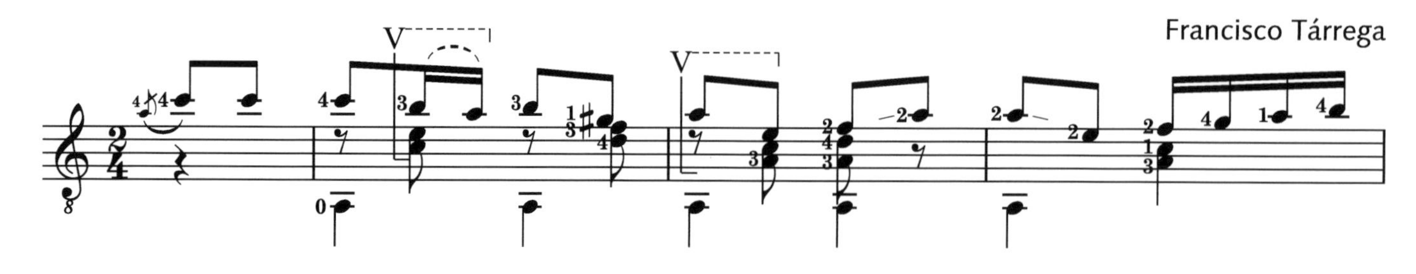

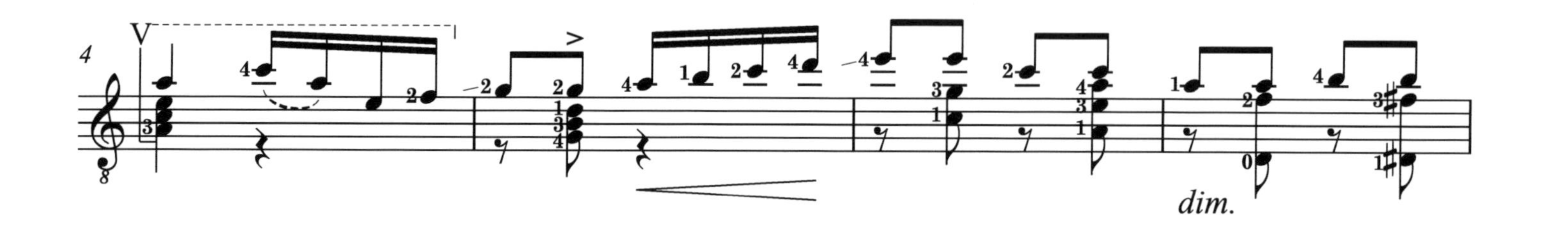

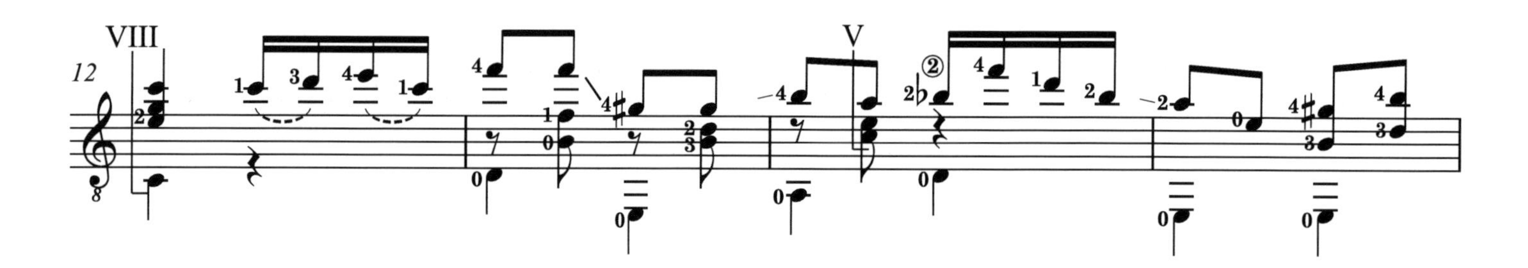

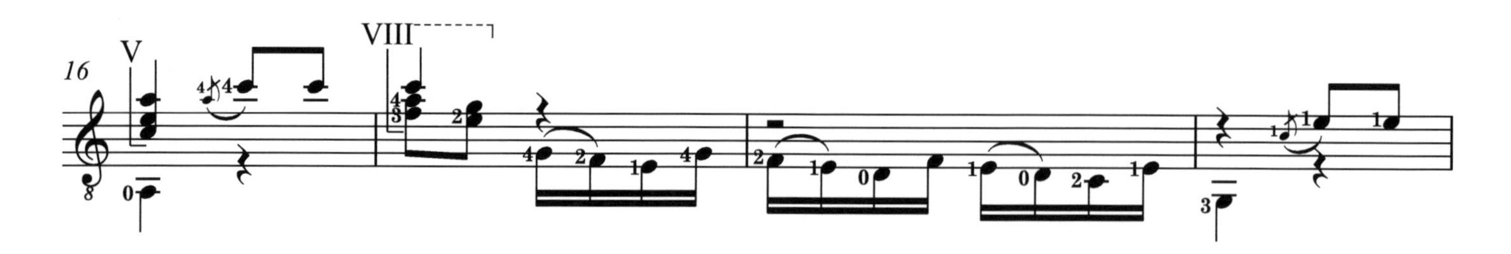

a tempo

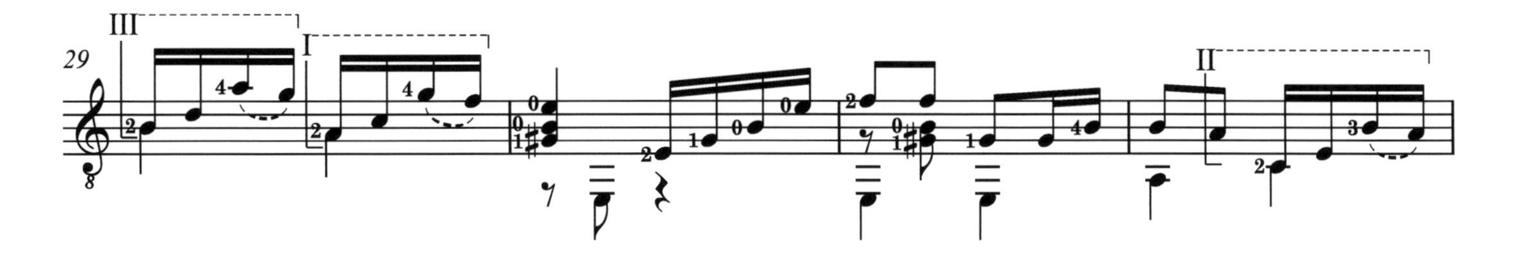

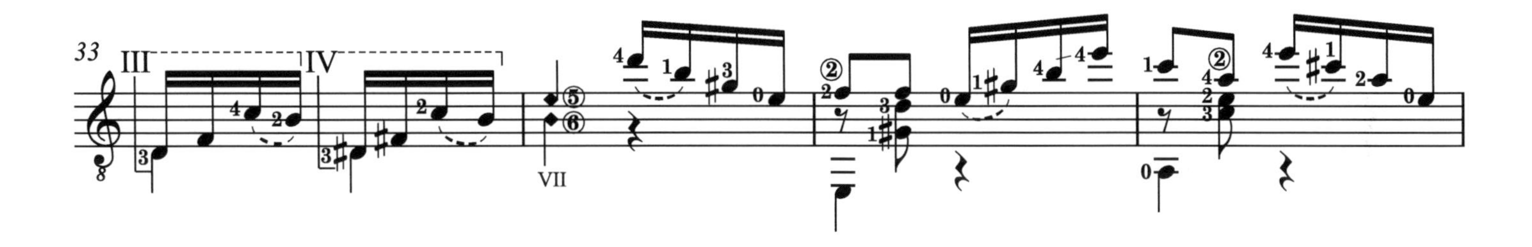

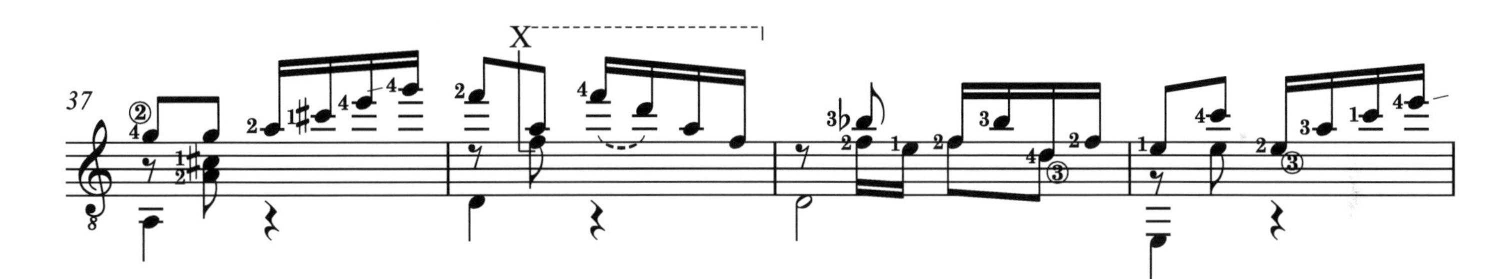

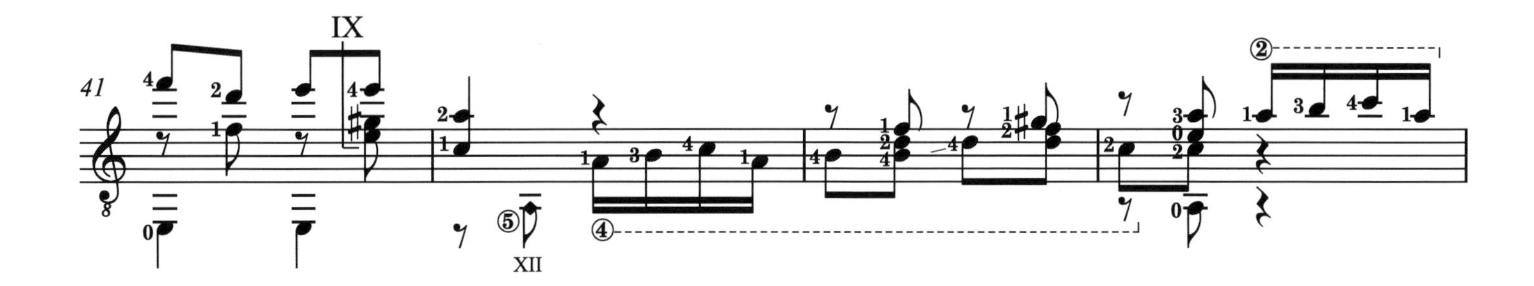

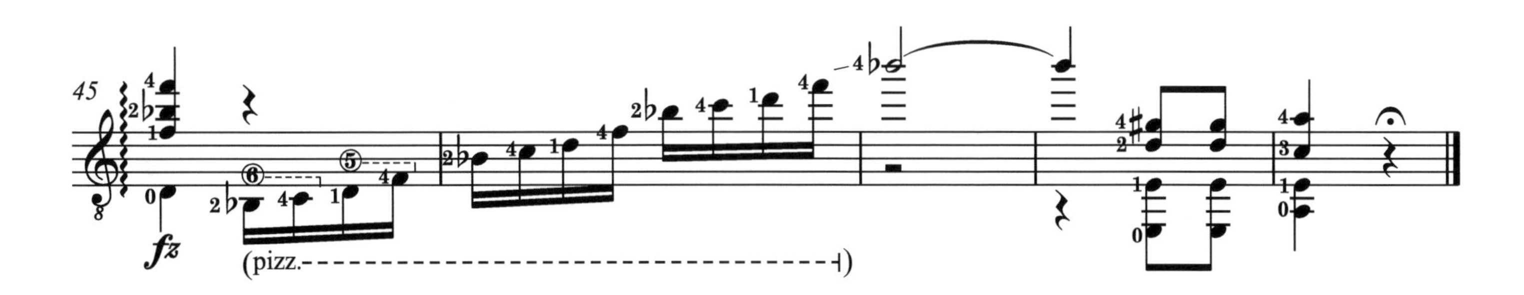
(pizz.

Las dos Hermanitas

Dos Valses para Guitarra

No. 1

Francisco Tárrega

No. 2

Malaguenà fácil

Francisco Tárrega

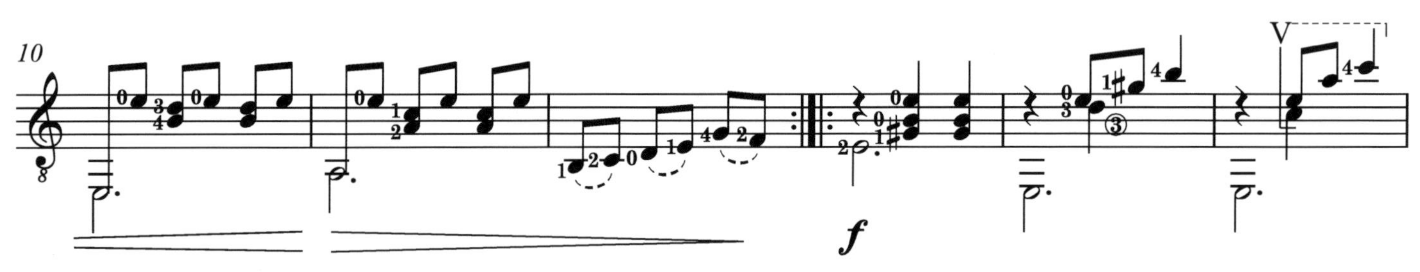

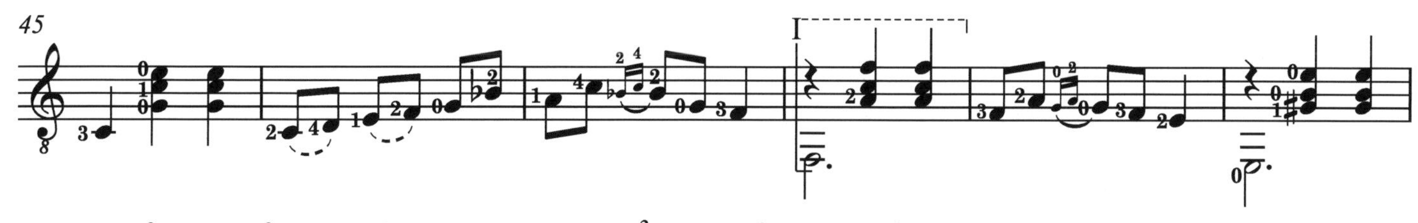

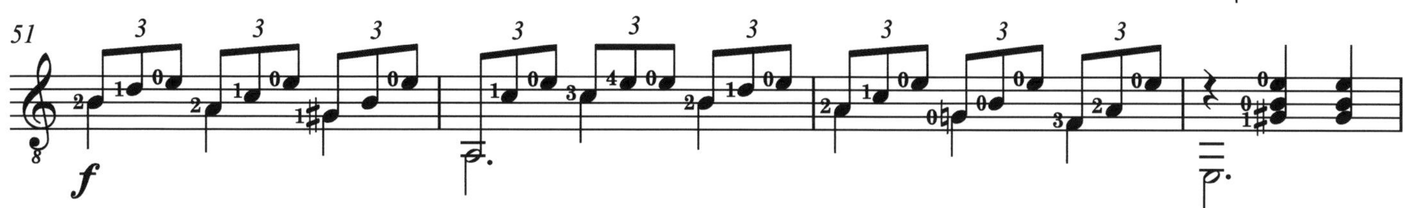

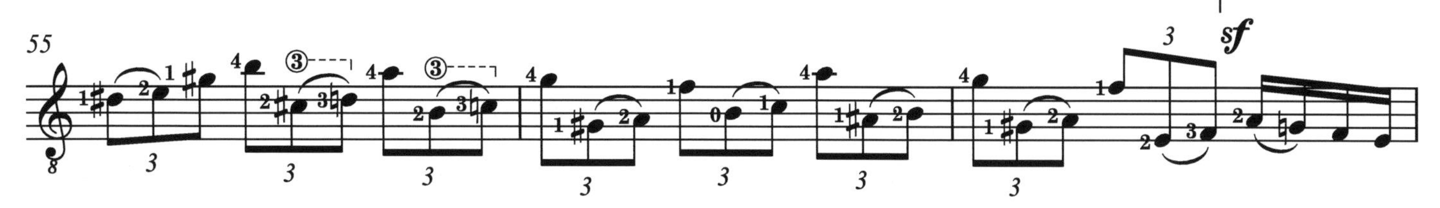

Copla

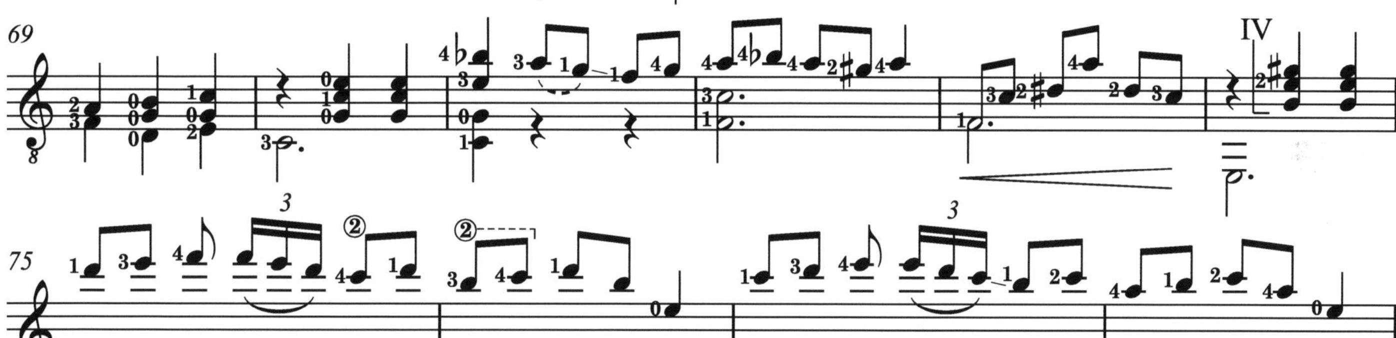

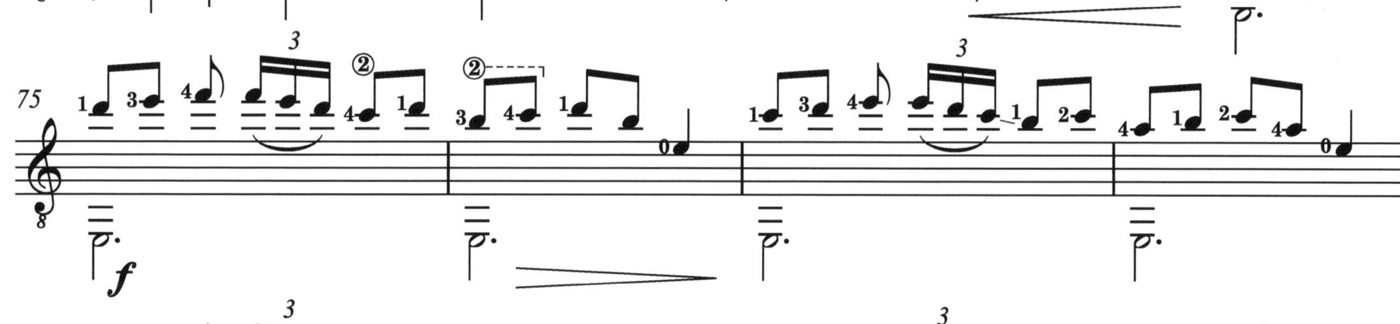

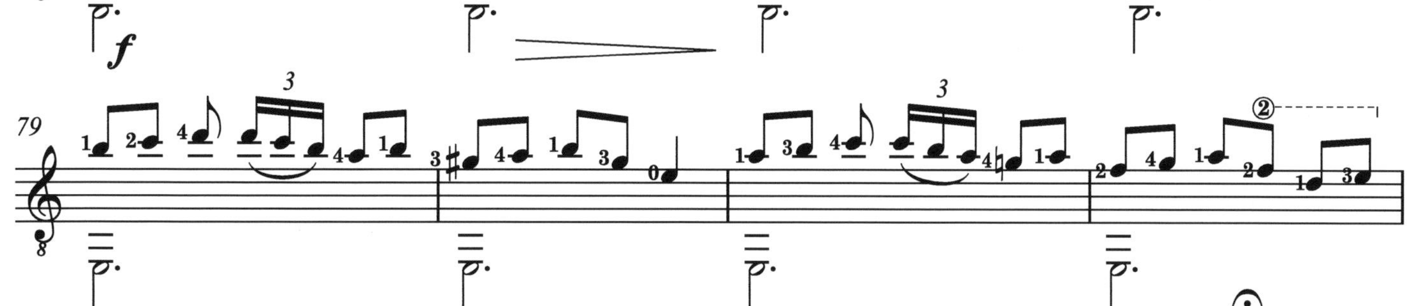

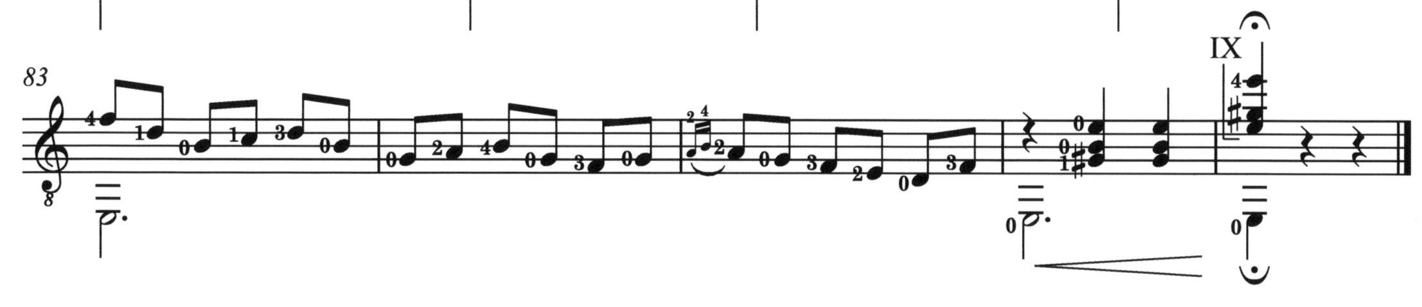

Mazurka

Francisco Tárrega

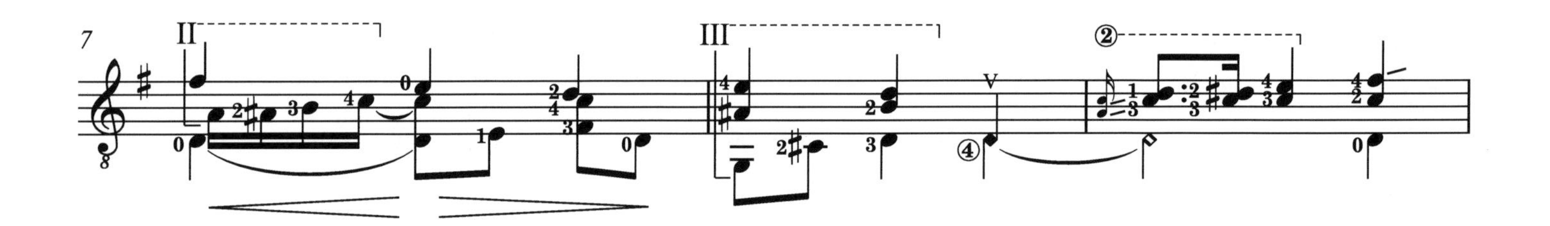

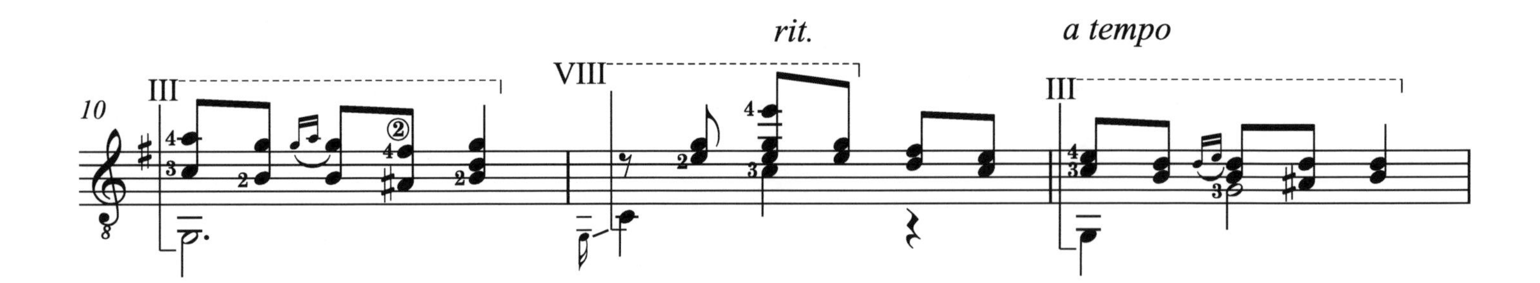

17
VII

20
II

rit.
a tempo
23
V

26
II

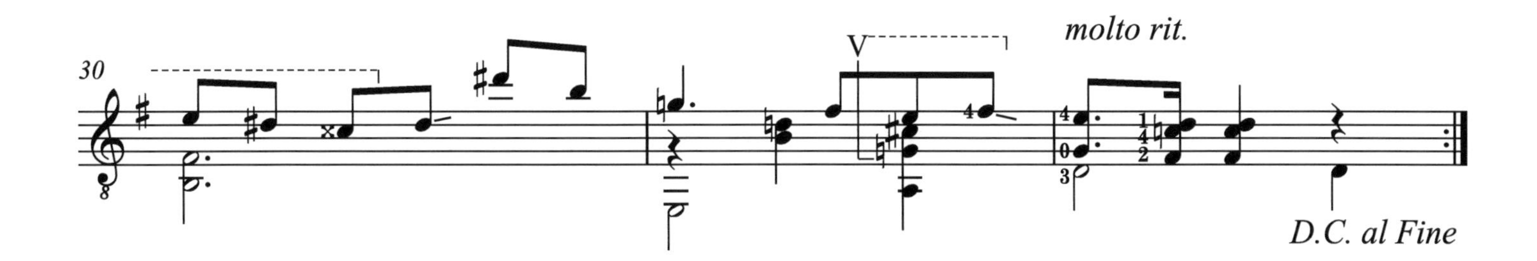
molto rit.
30
V
D.C. al Fine

Preludio en re menor

Moderato

Francisco Tárrega

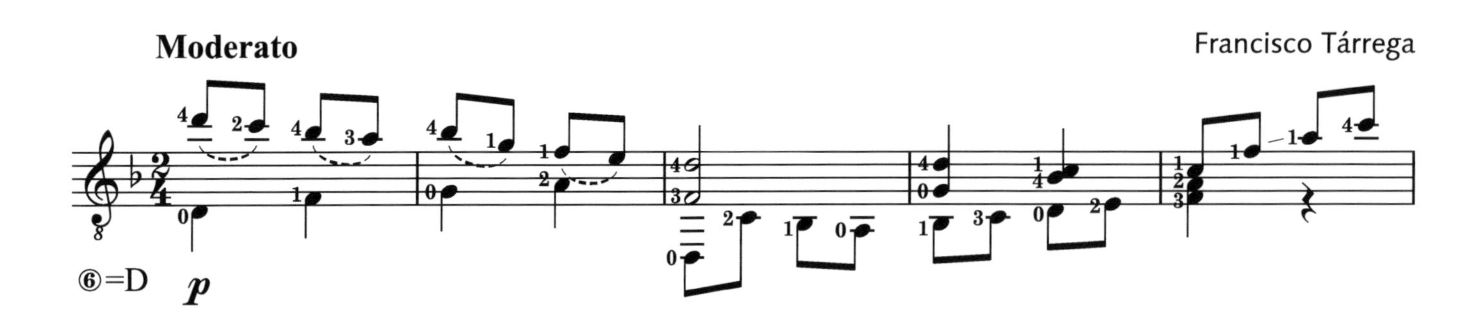

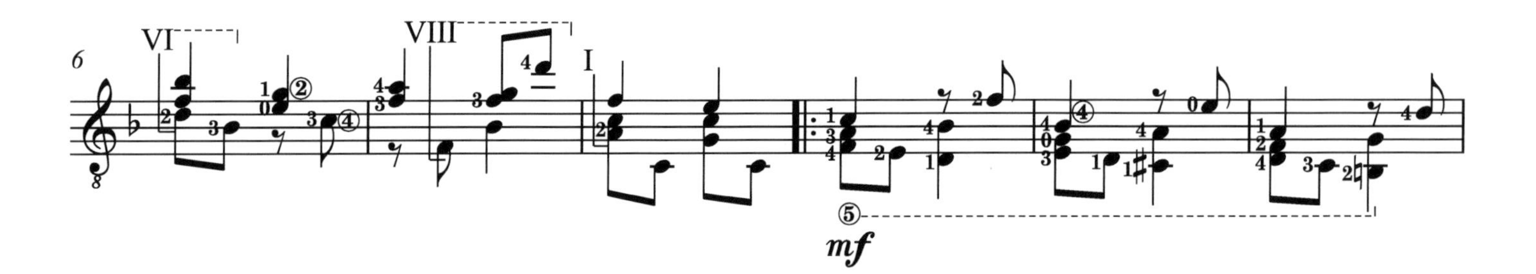

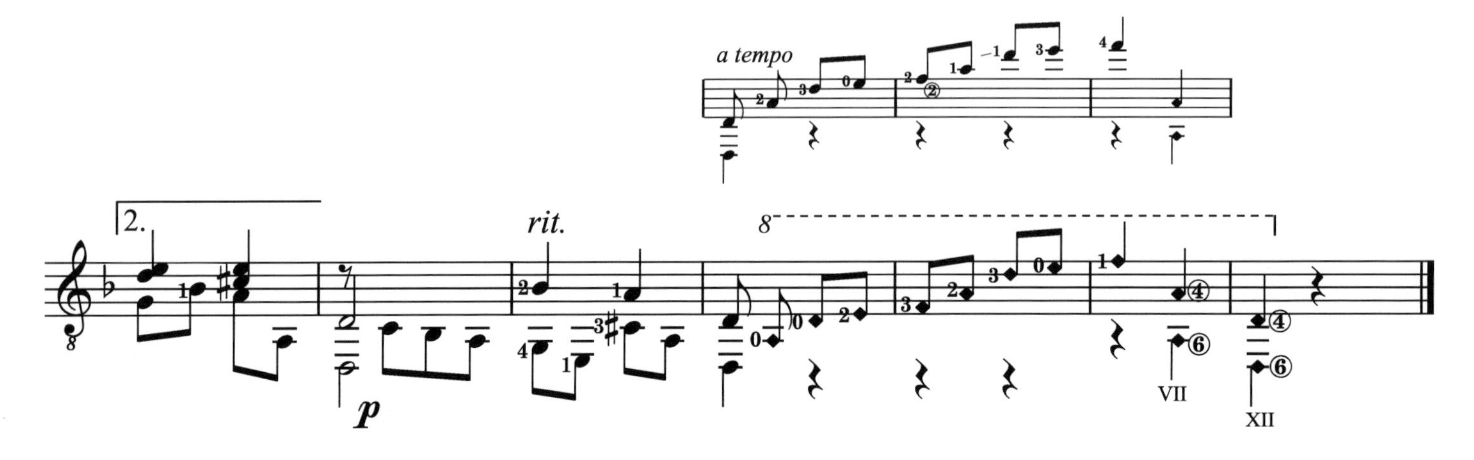